Remarkable WOMEN IN VERSE

THE SMALL BOOK OF BIG ACHIEVEMENTS

JULIA STEBBING

Sticky Bun PUBLISHING

FLORENCE NIGHTINGAL

HELEN KELLER •ROSA PARK

ANNE SULLIVAN •FLORENC

NIGHTINGALE •HELEN KELLE

ROSA PARKS •ANNE SULLIVA

FLORENCE NIGHTINGAL

HELEN KELLER •ROSA PARK

ANNE SULLIVAN •FLORENCE NIGHTINGAL

HELEN KELLER •ROSA PARK

ANNE SULLIVAN • FLORENC

NIGHTINGALE•HELEN

KELLER •ROSA PARKS •ANN

SULLIVAN •FLORENCE NIGHTINGAL

HELEN KELLER •ROSA PARK

ANNE SULLIVAN •FLORENCE NIGHTINGAL

HELEN KELLER •ROSA PARK

ROSA

1913 – 2005

Ku Klux Klan · Whites Only · Civil Rights · 381 Days

Martin Luther King · Segregation

Diploma · Jim Crow Laws

All children are special but who can say
Which child will change the world one day?
Who knows how far a child will go
When they are older? Does greatness show?

ROSA'S CHILDHOOD

It's Tuskegee, Alabama, nineteen thirteen
When Rosa McCauley arrives on the scene.
Parents James and Leona, carpenter and teacher,
Go to church every Sunday and pray with the preacher.

After Leona gives birth to Rosa's brother
Daddy walks out. They move with grandmother
To her farm in Pine Level. Rosa is two.
Back then what else could poor single mums do?

Growing up she is sickly, small, uncomplicated.
At eleven goes to school to become educated
In a one-room schoolhouse only black children attended.
Doesn't mix with white children, so white folks aren't offended.

Rosa sees white children bussed to school each day.
Black children always walk, they don't have a say,
Taught in shabby run-down buildings with teachers poorly paid,
No escape from deprivation without the highest grade.

Black children go to school five months a year, that is all.
The other months they toil from dawn till nightfall
Picking cotton in the fields, some are only four.
These people are cheap labour, no-one cares about the poor.

Remember what she does, remember her name,
And ask yourself, "Could I ever do the same?"

In the twenties life is tough, especially if black.
Rosa's always on her guard in fear of an attack.
There are lynchings and burnings and the racist Ku Klux Klan
Hide faces under pointy hoods to hunt down the black man.

For too long many white folk judged themselves superior,
Always treating black folk as though they are inferior.
Rosa's not ashamed of the colour of her skin.
The fight against prejudice is yet to begin.

AFTER ROSA LEAVES SCHOOL

When Rosa is sixteen grandmother falls sick.
She must stop education and leave school real quick
To care for grandmother, and then mother too.
That's what poor children were brought up to do.

Diligent and capable, her confidence now growing,
Rosa finds the time to learn typing and sewing.
Remember what she does, remember her name,
And ask yourself, "Could I ever do the same?"

Rosa marries Raymond Parks in nineteen thirty two,
Both involved in civil rights, so much for them to do.
With Raymond's encouragement his wife goes back to school
And receives her diploma, stays discreet, keeps her cool.

If you're black and want to vote you must take a test.
Three attempts it takes to pass and Rosa feels blessed.
She gladly teaches others how to do the same,
Restoring dignity and igniting a flame.

Working as a seamstress in a large department store,
You can be quite sure those she sews for are not poor.
Each day in Montgomery she observes discrimination
Where blacks are treated differently because of segregation.

Discrimination, segregation, it all means the same:
It's suppression of the blacks to fill their hearts with shame.
Different schools, separate washrooms, lack of freedom and choice.
It's pointless Rosa crying out, for who will hear her voice?

Montgomery and the southern states enforce Jim Crow laws,
Devised to help black people, but these laws have many flaws –
Promoting equal opportunities which either don't exist
Or are grossly second-rate. How are folks meant to resist?

The state of African-American lives should be deplored,
Downtrodden and impoverished, why are they so ignored?
Remember what she does, remember her name,
And ask yourself, "Could I ever do the same?"

WHAT ROSA DOES NEXT

It's the first of December nineteen fifty five,
Just a routine day, one more day to survive.
It's time to go home and Rosa boards a bus,
Sits down quietly, without any fuss.

Allowed to stay there if no white man has to stand,
But the bus soon fills up, and though nothing is planned
The driver, James Blake, tells those in Rosa's row
That the back of the bus is where they must go.

He orders them once and bellows once more,
"Get out of your seat! What are you waiting for?"
Other passengers look away, not wanting to get involved,
Hoping the situation is rapidly resolved.

Rosa sits impassively, doesn't move an inch.
Even when he barks again she does not flinch.
She is more than tired, she feels completely drained,
And Rosa is no longer prepared to be constrained.

Sitting there she recalls how twelve years before
That same driver yelled at her to use the rear door
And as she got off to re-board – she'd already paid her fare,
He sped off without a backward glance and left her standing there.

Blake calls the police to make sure Rosa is arrested.
When she's carted off to jail, not one passenger protested.
Rosa remains dignified, yet greatly annoyed
By the strong-arm tactics the police have employed.

News soon hits the streets of what Rosa Parks has done,
Earning admiration and approval of everyone.
Although convicted of defying segregation laws
She appeals the fourteen dollar fine. At last she's found her cause.

What Rosa Achieves

Rosa Parks' refusal to move or be intimidated
Is why the boycott of the buses is initiated.
To make sure this boycott will eventually succeed
Martin Luther King is brought in to take the lead.

Together with lawyers the decision is made
That blacks will not ride buses and will not be afraid.
For the first time ever a peaceful demonstration
Seeks to bring an end to this kind of segregation.

Forty thousand people make the choice to ignore
All public transportation, and though poor and footsore
They boycott the buses for three hundred and eighty one days.
Despite their exhaustion, their hearts are ablaze.

The Montgomery Bus Boycott in the USA
Inspires the civil rights movement, relevant today.
It takes thirteen months for the Supreme Court to declare
Segregation on buses is illegal and unfair.

Rosa Parks' decision not to stand but stay seated
Sets discrimination on its path towards being defeated.
At last African-Americans unite with one voice,
Changing the course of history, thanks to Rosa's choice.

Tell me, how many people can stand tall and proclaim
They changed the world without seeking fame?
How many people can ever admit
They improved the world, even just a bit?
Rosa fought for civil rights until her dying day.
No greater grace and bravery did anyone display.

Who knows how far a child will go
When they are older? Does greatness show?
Remember what she does, remember her name,
And ask yourself, "Could I ever do the same?"

GLOSSARY

deprivation	poverty
toil	hard work
lynchings	to hang by the neck
prejudice	intolerance, discrimination, narrow-mindedness
diligent	hard-working
civil rights	political and social freedom and equality for each person
grossly second-rate	for black people work opportunities were less and very few owned their own home because of harsh property qualifications
deplored	condemned, criticised
initiated	started
Martin Luther King	African-American minister and activist, famous for his contribution towards the civil rights movement from 1955 until his assassination in 1968

FLORENCE NIGHTINGALE
HELEN KELLER • ROSA PARK
ANNE SULLIVAN • FLORENC
NIGHTINGALE • HELEN KELLE
ROSA PARKS • ANNE SULLIVA
FLORENCE NIGHTINGALE
HELEN KELLER • ROSA PARK
ANNE SULLIVAN • FLORENCE NIGHTINGAL
HELEN KELLER • ROSA PARK
ANNE SULLIVAN • FLORENCE
NIGHTINGALE • HELEN
KELLER • ROSA PARKS • ANN
SULLIVAN • FLORENCE NIGHTINGAL
HELEN KELLER • ROSA PARK
ANNE SULLIVAN • FLORENCE NIGHTINGAL
HELEN KELLER • ROSA PARK

HELEN
1880-1968

Wah-Wah · Deaf · Blind · Mug

Hairbrush · Alexander Bell

Graduation · Braille · Tewksbury Almshouse

ANNE
1866-1936

HELEN

Eyes tightly closed, fingers jammed in each ear.
What can you see, tell me what can you hear?
A deep pit of darkness, so deep there's no sound.
This is the world to which Helen is bound.

In Tuscumbia, Alabama, eighteen eighty the year
When Helen is born, and it is quite clear
She is a clever child right from the start,
Walking at twelve months, both sassy and smart.

What joy she brings parents, Arthur and Kate,
She's pretty and funny, likes to imitate.
The Kellers are proud of their six-month-old daughter
Who plainly says 'tea' and 'wah-wah' for water.

Their home, a small house on a farm, Ivy Green,
Has the prettiest garden you've ever seen,
Where Helen amuses herself for hours
Climbing an oak tree, picking wild flowers.

At nineteen months Helen falls ill with a fever
But quick as it comes, the fever will leave her.
When the sickness is gone her parents grow aware
Helen can't see or hear and are filled with despair.

The idyllic childhood that Helen has known
Abruptly departs like a bird that has flown
Far from its nest, with no sense of direction.
A sense of confusion, no outside connection.

Eyes tightly closed, fingers jammed in each ear.
What can you see, tell me what can you hear?
A deep pit of darkness, so deep there's no sound.
This is the world to which Helen is bound.

This once happy child grows disruptive, depressive.
Whenever thwarted, her aggression's excessive.
She screams long and loud knowing she'll win
And get what she wants, parents always give in.

They move to a larger house on their estate,
Cook's daughter, Martha Washington, her new playmate.
What fun in the kitchen with ice cream and dough,
Helen, the leader, with Martha in tow.

She invents sixty hand signals all on her own
So she can join in and not feel so alone.
Her disturbing behaviour is difficult to bear.
She won't eat with a spoon, button boots, wash her hair.

The Kellers aren't sure to whom they can turn,
Convinced there's much more their Helen can learn.
Her father consults a Baltimore physician
Who humbly admits he can't cure her condition.

He invites them to meet inventor Alexander Bell,
An expert in deaf children, with wife and mother deaf as well.
Bell is so moved by the parents' desperation
He suggests Michael Anagnos to help their situation.

ANNE

Anne Sullivan can scarcely distinguish day from night.
How hard it must have been, at five, to lose most of her sight.
Three years later mummy dies and daddy sends her away
With brother Jimmie to a poorhouse. There's nowhere else to stay.

The Tewksbury Almshouse is unclean, dilapidated,
Jam-packed with the poor, the sick, the intoxicated.
The homeless mix with criminals, children are neglected,
But Anne takes all this in her stride and does not seem affected.

Three months after they arrive, brother Jimmie dies.
Anne's consumed with rage she cannot disguise,
Until one day, quite by chance, she's delighted
To find a room full of books. At last she's excited!

People read to her and she learns about schools
Where she can study and live by new rules.
When Inspectors visit to investigate conditions,
Anne speaks up bravely to reveal her ambitions.

At fourteen Anne goes to a school for the blind,
At first she's ashamed that her learning lags behind.
She's never owned a hairbrush, doesn't know how to sew.
There's so much to be taught, but how would she know?

When her schooling begins Anne's a very naughty child
And the teachers can't cope with a pupil so wild.
Girls from better backgrounds make her feel humiliated.
Even by the teachers she feels intimidated.

Anne's knowledge increases, her confidence grows
And soon she is loved by everyone she knows.
The operations on her eyes help improve her sight.
Eventually she learns to read, though she still cannot write.

Anne is clever, works hard, has self-motivation,
And is chosen to speak at the class graduation.
"Duty bids us go forth into active life," she cries
As her voice rings out loud and clear, soaring to the skies.

Principal Michael Anagnos knows what to do
On receiving a letter out of the blue,
Seeking help for Helen Keller, who at seven-years-old
Is blind and deaf and rarely does what she is told.

Mr Anagnos realises Anne will be suitable.
(She is very capable, her references indisputable).
So that is how in the year eighteen eighty-seven
Helen meets Anne, 'a match made in heaven'.

HELEN AND ANNE

Anne sets out the rules that Helen must obey
But Helen, lacking self-control, wants everything her way.
Whenever Helen shouts and screams the Kellers intervene.
For Helen to be taught to 'speak' she needs a change of scene.

Driving horse and carriage in circles, Helen cannot tell
Anne is taking her to the cottage where she used to dwell.
Helen doesn't know where she is, just as Anne has planned.
Resolving Helen will learn to 'speak' Anne takes her firmly in hand.

Anne constantly taps Helen's palm to spell out a word,
Reciting what each letter is, yet her voice remains unheard.
Whatever Anne tries to sign Helen finds mystifying,
Failing to grasp exactly what those letters are signifying.

'Milk' and 'mug' mean different things. Why can't Anne teach her
Neither word means 'to drink'? How is she to reach her?
Anne makes Helen hold a mug while drawing from the well,
Pumping water on Helen's other hand, to feel it as it fell.

Water pours through Helen's fingers as Anne signs
w-a-t-e-r,
As though liquid makes an imprint, leaving behind a scar.
Into her head, like a lightning jolt, springs an image so profound.
Helen stands transfixed and emits a primal sound.

"Wah-wah," she cries as at last a light is turned on in her mind.
"Wah-wah," as she makes the connection. She can't see yet is no longer
blind.
She falls upon objects around her, Anne rapidly signs to each one.
In that one defining moment Helen's new life has begun.

Helen devours each fresh word with tremendous passion,
Extending her vocabulary, words her latest fashion.
Anne teaches her to read Braille as well as sign by hand,
Pouring knowledge into her pupil like an hourglass filling with sand.

There is so much more to Helen than a girl who's deaf and blind.
She becomes a strong, ambitious woman refusing to be confined.
The first deaf-blind person to earn a college degree,
An author, lecturer, activist – outstanding don't you agree?

Helen falls in love with Patrick Fagan, to her parent's great dismay.
He's a reporter come to work with her. She has never felt this way.
They put an end to their daughter's romance, perhaps doomed from the start.
Who can believe a deaf-blind woman can fall in love with all her heart?

Anne is teacher and governess and for years Helen's closest friend.
It's Helen who's beside her when Anne's life draws to an end.
They both overcame adversity with their courage and grace,
Helen and Anne together made the world a better place.

Eyes tightly closed, fingers jammed in each ear.
What can you see, tell me what can you hear?
A deep pit of darkness, so deep there's no sound.
This is the world to which Helen was bound.

GLOSSARY

dilapidated	run-down
intoxicated	drunk
intimidated	overawed, overwhelmed
thwarted	obstructed, hindered, let down

FLORENCE NIGHTINGALE
HELEN KELLER • ROSA PARK
ANNE SULLIVAN • FLORENC
NIGHTINGALE • HELEN KELLE
ROSA PARKS • ANNE SULLIVA
FLORENCE NIGHTINGALE
HELEN KELLER • ROSA PARK
ANNE SULLIVAN • FLORENCE NIGHTINGAL
HELEN KELLER • ROSA PARK
ANNE SULLIVAN • FLORENC
NIGHTINGALE • HELEN
KELLER • ROSA PARKS • ANN
SULLIVAN • FLORENCE NIGHTINGAL
HELEN KELLER • ROSA PARK
ANNE SULLIVAN • FLORENCE NIGHTINGAL
HELEN KELLER • ROSA PARK

FLORENCE

1820-1910

Rats and Mice · Blood · Crimean War

Wash Your Hands · Decimals · Lice

Fractions · Nurse's Uniform · Filth

FLORENCE GROWING UP

Can you imagine yourself in the age
When men are in charge, and girls cannot engage
In everyday things we now take for granted?
No wonder some young girls become disenchanted.

They learn how to sew, paint, sing and dance
But the three Rs aren't given a chance.
Domesticity their mind's occupation,
A respectable marriage their sole expectation.

The scene is now set as I open my tale
Of that super-achiever, Florence Nightingale.
Her wealthy parents spend three years abroad
On honeymoon in Europe which they could afford.

Born eighteen twenty in Florence, Italy, hence her name,
When her parents missed home, back to England they came
With older sister Parthenope, born the year before,
To a life of privilege, who could ask for more?
Winters in Embley Park entertaining till late,
Long summers at Lea Hurst, their second estate.

Both sisters, well-taught by their father, at home,
Learn languages, history, to explain a palindrome.
Florence excels in science and mathematics,
Absorbing permutations from equations to quadratics.

Mr and Mrs Nightingale mix with elite society,
Generous hosts leading lives with genial propriety.
Parthenope takes to partying like a duck takes to water,
Pretty, sociable yet demure, a true Victorian daughter.

Florence fails to find delight in such social events,
Feeling awkward and uneasy, to her they make no sense.
Showing little interest in the usual social whirl,
She prefers her studies, this thoughtful, studious girl.

What she enjoys most is caring for the poor
And for those who are ailing, she strives to do more.
Her mother finds her daughter hard to understand,
While Florence doesn't want the life that mother's planned.

For seven years poet Richard Monckton Milnes pursues her,
But she remains unmoved - perhaps his poetry doesn't amuse her.
Henry Nicholson, her cousin, totally adores her,
But Florence doesn't feel the same, however he implores her.
You'd not believe how many tears her family shed
When Florence says her mind's made up, she doesn't want to wed.

At seventeen she hears God's voice telling her to be a nurse.
Her parents think she's lost her mind and believe there's nothing worse.
It's common knowledge that is how poor women make a living.
Florence does not listen, filling her parents with misgiving.

For girls from wealthy backgrounds, work isn't the convention,
And however much her parents object, she pays them no attention.
Friend Sidney Herbert explains how the rich should help the poor,
And these few words of wisdom support her even more.

It takes another seven years for father to relent.
She attends Kaiserswerth Institute, what joy is his consent.
Studying nursing just three months, in awe of all she learns,
She finds the true love of her life, and inside a fire burns.

FLORENCE BECOMES A NURSE

When Florence returns to London a friend requests her aid
In a nursing home for gentlewomen, although she won't be paid.
Finally, Mr Nightingale decides the time has come
To pay her five hundred pounds a year, those days a princely sum.

Arriving at the home she finds only Protestants admitted
And insists that all faiths be allowed, so more women benefitted.
The filthy bedding, rats and mice are totally depressing
But in her single-minded way she finds hard work a blessing.
To shift food and medicines between floors dumbwaiters are installed
Helping reduce the chaos by which Florence is appalled.

Patients are asked to ring a bell when they need attention,
A simple idea, you might think, but then a new invention.
These poor retired women, in Florence they find a friend,
Giving money to the needy and caring till the end.

Cholera comes to London, Florence's help is sought once more,
This time in Middlesex hospital where survival rates are poor.
With no recognised treatment, who is there to advise
That this disease is caused by tainted water supplies?

Fear of catching cholera becomes such a dreadful strain
That many nurses leave their job, too frightened to remain.
Florence never shares her water, understanding good hygiene.
While other nurses pass away, she survives by keeping clean.

FLORENCE JOINS THE WAR

In the year eighteen fifty-four Great Britain joins with France,
And Turkey and Sardinia in order to advance
The success of the Crimean war, a bloodthirsty event,
Where battles against Russia are fought with great intent.

Nine hundred thousand soldiers never will return,
So many men from all sides, will the Generals ever learn?
The few hospitals in Turkey are overwhelmed and cannot cope,
Patients are given atrocious care and very little hope.

Sidney Herbert asks Florence to help tend to the sick.
Straightaway she starts to plan, it's crucial to be quick.
She arrives with thirty-eight nurses in Scutari within three days
Where they're thrust into a hellish world of incompetence and malaise.

At first doctors prove hostile, putting up resistance.
She pays them no attention, she's here to give assistance.
Ignoring their sexist attitude which in those days is the norm,
She rolls up her sleeves and gets to work, never one to conform.

The scenes that confront her are utterly horrific
And to get the full picture, it's best to be specific.
Soldiers sleep in flea-ridden beds, or straw mats on the floor.
Such blood and filth and squalor she'd never seen before.
Too few dressings, overcrowding, lack of food and medication,
Bedding and clothing in short supply, a world of human degradation.
The stench is overwhelming, and pitiful amputees
Cry out in pain, terrified, for care and expertise.

Florence sets about improving standards of hygiene.
How can patients hope to recover in places so unclean?
More people dying on the wards than ever on the field.
She assumes her obligation to make sure they are healed.

Florence has the passion and the drive to get things done.
Leading by example she mucks in with everyone,
Scrubbing clothes the injured wear, washing bodies covered in lice,
Taking charge and, at the same time, giving calm and sound advice.

Sewers beneath the wards are totally outdated,
Swarming with large rodents, the water contaminated.
Vile vermin are flushed out, ventilation improved,
And the death rate decreases as toxic germs are removed.

Florence and her team never give in to despair,
Working *twenty-four/seven* to end this nightmare.
Roaming the corridors with her lamp to sounds of wounded crying,
Florence seeks out the frightened and brings comfort to the dying.

FLORENCE RETURNS HOME

Florence contracts brucellosis at the end of the war,
Perhaps from infected milk or meat, there's no way to be sure.
Often in pain and confined to bed, the diagnosis undecided,
Some call her a hyphochondriac, she's both admired and derided.

But Florence doesn't focus on what people do or say,
However stubborn and perverse, she likes to have her way.
She compiles a lengthy war report on what had taken place
And statistician William Farr helps her to make the case.

With charts, maths and statistics she can verify
Poor hygiene, not poor nutrition, is why the soldiers die.
Florence founds a training school where nursing will be taught,
But cannot do it by herself due to illness she has caught.
Learning to delegate, she brings in new regulations,
New ideas and designs, more modern innovations.
'The Lady With the Lamp', as Florence is now known,
Shines fresh light on health reforms, as history has shown.

In nursing, without any doubt, Florence is a pioneer,
Leading with strong purpose throughout her long career,
Transforming the world of medicine in a major revolution,
Sanitation and good food just part of her contribution.

She links poor hygiene to the spread of infection.
It's astounding no-one previously had made this connection!
Way before the advent of womens' emancipation
She improves the general welfare in every situation.

In her later years she still retained a brilliant mind,
Continuing with her lifelong work even after going blind.
A resolute, independent woman, filled with good intent,
And a figure of authority, to a very great extent.
Forward-thinking and dynamic, an amazing inspiration,
A credit to herself, her family and her nation.

GLOSSARY

the three Rs	reading, writing and arithmetic (the third R comes from saying 'rithmetic')
Parthenope	named after an early Greek settlement, which was re-founded as Neapolis, and is now Napoli in Italian, or Naples as we call it
palindrome	letters of the alphabet which read the same forwards as backwards, e.g. refer, minim, level
permutations	the number of ways a collection of items can be arranged, e.g. ABC, ACB, BCA, CBA, CAB, BAC
quadratics	a mathematical problem that deals with a variable multiplied by itself
ailing	unwell, sickly
convention	custom, habit
Kaiserswerth Institute	their training system was a close parallel to the educational system for nurses that we see today
gentlewomen	women of noble birth or good social standing
Protestants	second-largest form of Christianity
cholera	infectious disease which can lead to dehydration and even death if untreated; caused by eating contaminated food or drinking water (potentially fatal bacterial disease spread by contaminated water, now rarely found)

Crimean War	a war fought from October 1853 to February 1856 in which Russia lost to an alliance made up of the Ottoman Empire, the UK, Sardinia and France
malaise	discontent, anxiety, illness
degradation	filth, squalor
amputees	those who have lost a limb
brucellosis	a highly contagious disease caused by drinking unpasteurised milk or eating undercooked meat from infected animals
hypochondriac	someone who lives in fear they are seriously ill, even though they are not
derided	mocked, scorned
pioneer	forerunner, discoverer, creator
sanitation	cleanliness
emancipation	freeing a person from another person's control:

Sticky Bun Publishing
www.stickybunpublishing.com
Second Edition,
ISBN: 978-1-8382652-1-2

Printed in Great Britain
by Amazon

86241708R10018